Determiners

Transitive
Verbs

Gerunds

Infinitive

hrases

ENGLISH

GRAMMAR

for Students

workbook

Answer Key

Compo
Senten

estion
Tags

count
ouns

Adjecti
Phras

Reflexive
Pronouns

Clauses

ENGLISH GRAMMAR for Students workbook

Answer Key

LEARNERS PUBLISHING

© 2002 Learners Publishing Pte Ltd

First published 2002 by **Learners Publishing Pte Ltd**
222 Tagore Lane, #03-01 TG Building, Singapore 787603

Reprinted 2002 (three times), 2003 (three times), 2004 (twice), 2005 (twice)

Email: learnpub@learners.com.sg
Visit our website: http://www.learners.com.sg

ISBN 981 4070 44 0

Printed by B & Jo Enterprise Pte Ltd, Singapore

ASSOCIATE COMPANIES

R I C Learners International Limited
P.O. Box 332, Greenwood
WESTERN AUSTRALIA 6924

R I C Publications Limited (Asia)
5th floor, Gotanda Mikado Building
2-5-8 Hiratsuka, Shinagawa-ku Tokyo
JAPAN 142-0051
Tel: 03-3788-9201
Fax: 03-3788-9202
Email: elt@ricpublications.com
Website: www.ricpublications.com

Learners Educational Publishing Sdn Bhd
43A, Jalan 34/154 Taman Delima
56000 Cheras, Kuala Lumpur
MALAYSIA
Tel: 603-9100-1868
Fax: 603-9102-4730
Email: enquiry@learners.com.my

PREFACE

This workbook has been written primarily for students using **English Grammar for Students** and gives them an opportunity of testing themselves on the grammatical concepts introduced and explained in that book. At the same time, the full explanations given in the introduction to each exercise mean that it may be used as an independent self-testing tool.

There are 40 units, each containing four sets of exercises, graded for difficulty from A to D. Each exercise contains 8 to 16 questions, which vary from straightforward to fairly challenging. The first answer (in some cases the first two or three) is usually provided, so that the student has clear guidance as to the kind of answer expected. All the answers are given in the **Answer Key**.

The order of the units follows roughly the order of topics in **English Grammar for Students**, but some closely related topics that are dealt with in separate chapters in that book are here brought into closer association. The intention has also been to expand and develop some of the grammatical points made in **English Grammar for Students**, so that users not only consolidate what they have learnt but also widen their knowledge.

Compiling these exercises has been an enjoyable exercise in itself, and I hope students will in turn enjoy the challenge of doing them.

I would like to thank George Davidson for timely help in the final stages of compilation.

Anne Seaton

Edinburgh 2001

1 PLURAL FORMS

A
2.	volcanoes	3.	halves	4.	jockeys
5.	libraries	6.	buses	7.	knives
8.	zoos	9.	zeroes or zeros	10.	addresses
11.	loaves	12.	roofs		

B
1.	geese	2.	teeth	3.	reindeer
4.	feet	5.	women, children	6.	mice
7.	humans	8.	aircraft	9.	chessmen
10.	oxen				

C
2.	pair of binoculars	3.	pair of slippers
4.	pairs of chopsticks	5.	pair of pants
6.	pair of running shorts	7.	pairs of scissors
8.	pairs of eyes	9.	pair of swimming goggles
10.	pair of pyjamas	11.	pair of sunglasses
12.	pairs of jeans		

D
2.	are/were	3.	do/ does
4.	is/was	5.	are/were (or is/was)
6.	are/were (or is/was)	7.	leads
8.	have/has	9.	were
10.	are/were (or is/was)	11.	don't
12.	are/were	13.	need
14.	are/were (or is/was)		

2 COUNTABLE AND UNCOUNTABLE NOUNS

A
2. Steel is an important material.
3. Grandad's wearing a hat made of straw.
4. It's difficult to ride a bicycle in soft sand.
5. I'd like a cup of tea without milk or sugar.
6. You can cut cheese with a knife.
7. Water comes out of a tap.
8. An apple is a kind of fruit that grows on a tree.
9. Money is a useful thing to have.
10. If you want food there's soup and a sandwich here.
11. You need a pen and paper to write a letter.
12. Fujiyama is a high mountain with snow on top.

B
2.	any	3.	some, a	4.	any
5.	a, some	6.	any	7.	some
8.	some, an	9.	a, some	10.	a, any
11.	some, some	12.	some, an, some		

C
2.	sheet	3.	grain	4.	bottle
5.	stick	6.	drop	7.	lump
8.	slice	9.	loaf	10.	pane
11.	bar	12.	blade		

D
2.	stationery	3.	news	4.	fruit
5.	furniture	6.	information	7.	equipment
8.	work	9.	advice	10.	clothing

3 PROPER NOUNS

A Hi, Edward!

I hope you are well. We are spending Easter in Penang and we are having a lovely time. On Tuesday Jane and I went windsurfing with Dad and on Wednesday we went to the beach with Mum and had a swim in the sea. There's lots to do here and the weather is very good.

We shall be back in Singapore at the end of April. Have you finished your project about Napoleon? Miss Lee wants it back at the beginning of next term.

Jane sends her love to you. See you soon.

Peter

B
1.	the Eiffel Tower	2.	Mount Fuji
3.	Lake Superior	4.	the Leaning Tower of Pisa
5.	the United Kingdom	6.	the Statue of Liberty
7.	Great Britain	8.	the Grand Canyon
9.	the Black Sea	10.	New Delhi
11.	Tiananmen Square	12.	the Brahmaputra
13.	the Tower of London	14.	the Merlion
15.	the Indian Ocean	16.	the Philippines
17.	the North Pole	18.	the Gulf of Mexico
19.	the Andes	20.	the Arctic Circle

C
2. The Hunchback of Notre Dame
3. The Tale of Robin Hood
4. When the Machine Stopped
5. The Mouse that Roared
6. Treasure Island
7. Just William
8. Alice through the Looking Glass
9. The Babes in the Wood
10. Around the World in Eighty Days
11. King Solomon's Mines
12. My Family and Other Animals
13. The Wizard of Oz

D
3.	Americans	4.	the English	5.	Spain
6.	the Japanese	7.	Ireland	8.	the British
9.	Sweden	10.	Pakistanis	11.	Chile
12.	France	13.	Denmark	14.	Switzerland
15.	Belgians	16.	the Netherlands		
17.	the Portuguese	18.	Norway		

4 PRONOUNS AND DETERMINERS

A
2.	third person singular	3.	second person plural
4.	third person plural	5.	second person singular
6.	third person singular	7.	third person singular
8.	first person plural	9.	first person singular
10.	third person singular	11.	first person plural
12.	third person plural		

B
2.	he	3.	they	4.	her	5.	you
6.	it	7.	she	8.	I, you	9.	we
10.	I, us	11.	them	12.	him		

C
2.	myself	3.	themselves	4.	ourselves
5.	yourselves	6.	herself	7.	yourself
8.	itself	9.	myself	10.	itself
11.	themselves	12.	himself		

D
2.	his, hers	3.	its, theirs	4.	their, his
5.	your, mine	6.	your, ours	7.	our, theirs
8.	our, yours	9.	her, his	10.	your, mine

5 WHO, WHOM, WHICH and THAT

A
1.	who	2.	which	3.	who	4.	which
5.	who	6.	which	7.	who	8.	who
9.	which	10.	who	11.	which	12.	which

B
2.	What	3.	Who	4.	Which	5.	What
6.	Who	7.	Which	8.	What	9.	Which
10.	Who	11.	What	12.	Who	13.	Which
14.	Which						

C
3.	who	4.	whom	5.	Whom	6.	Who
7.	whom	8.	whom	9.	who	10.	whom
11.	whom	12.	who				

D
3.	whom	4.	that	5.	which	6.	that
7.	that	8.	which	9.	that	10.	that
11.	that	12.	whom				

6 DETERMINERS: THE ARTICLES

A
2.	a	3.	an	4.	a	5.	an
6.	a	7.	an	8.	an	9.	a
10.	a	12.	the	13.	the	14.	THE
15.	THE	16.	the	17.	the	18.	THE
19.	the	20.	THE				

B Helen looked in the cupboard in the kitchen for a tablecloth to put on the dining table. She found a pretty cloth with red spots. She spread the cloth over the table, and then she went to find the knives and forks and spoons to lay on the table ready for the meal. 'Lay an extra place,' said her mother, 'because Simon has invited a friend.' Helen put mats round the table and laid each place with a knife, a fork and a spoon. Then she gave everyone a glass. 'Shall I put a candle in the middle of the table?' she asked. 'If you can find a nice one,' said her mother.

Everybody came in and sat down at the table. They talked about the things they had done during the day. Helen had been working on a project at school. Simon had had a piano lesson. Mum had been to the dentist. Dad had been at the office all day. Simon's friend had a part in the school play and he had been rehearsing. When they had finished the meal, they turned on the television and watched the news. Then they saw a programme about the disappearance of wild animals from the world.

C
2.	enormous	3.	striped, dark grey	4.	orange
5.	smart new	6.	clean	7.	thickest
8.	easy	9.	orderly	10.	lucky, busy
11.	very lazy	12.	untidy		

D
1.	some	2.	a	3.	an	4.	any
5.	some	6.	a	7.	any	8.	a
9.	any	10.	some	11.	a	12.	a

7 ADJECTIVES(1)

A
- 4. The water is cold.
- 6. a kind nurse
- 8. tall trees
- 10. The dictionary is thick.
- 12. narrow streets
- 14. hardworking students
- 16. an interesting project
- 5. The pencil is blunt
- 7. The clouds are black.
- 9. The coffee is hot.
- 11. The king is powerful.
- 13. The drawing is clever.
- 15. The baby is sweet.

B
- 3. musical
- 6. dangerous
- 9. weekly
- 12. homeless
- 15. personal
- 4. selfish
- 7. dusty
- 10. artistic
- 13. comfortable
- 16. costly
- 5. rainy
- 8. peaceful
- 11. massive
- 14. successful

C
- 2. nervous
- 5. penniless
- 8. muddy
- 11. sunny
- 14. furious
- 3. beautiful
- 6. studious
- 9. playful
- 12. global
- 4. bridal
- 7. famous
- 10. noisy
- 13. easy

D
- 2. big thick academic
- 4. charming young Singaporean
- 6. noisy English
- 8. crazy American
- 10. high grey stone
- 12. long pointed yellow
- 3. tall narrow dark-green
- 5. small fluffy white
- 7. large square cardboard
- 9. nasty tiny red stinging
- 11. wonderful new geographical

8 ADJECTIVES(2)

A
- 2. intelligent
- 6. slender
- 10. extensive
- 3. wide
- 7. soft
- 11. easy
- 4. splendid
- 8. firm
- 12. studious
- 5. noisy
- 9. handsome

B
- 2. dull
- 6. light
- 10. graceful
- 3. gentle
- 7. narrow
- 11. short
- 4. thin
- 8. slow
- 12. hollow
- 5. stingy
- 9. early

C
- 3. more precious (two)
- 5. neatest (one)
- 7. quickest (one)
- 9. warmer (one)
- 11. most imaginative (five)
- 4. more cheerful (two)
- 6. more reasonable (four)
- 8. deepest (one)
- 10. more thrilling (two)
- 12. kindest (one)

D
- 2. handsomest
- 4. thinner
- 6. simplest
- 8. nicest
- 10. saddest
- 12. politest
- 3. farther or further
- 5. funniest
- 7. pleasantest
- 9. heavier
- 11. safest

9 VERBS: AM, IS, ARE

A
- 1. is
- 5. are
- 9. are
- 2. Are
- 6. Is
- 10. Is
- 3. am
- 7. am, is
- 11. Are
- 4. are
- 8. is
- 12. is

B
1. Dave's in the garden. He's on the swing.
2. Listen! There's a strange noise.
3. Where's Sally? She's wanted on the phone.
4. Have one of these cherries. They're very sweet.
5. What's for dinner today? I hope it's noodles.
6. You're wrong — that's a porpoise, not a dolphin.
7. I'm in the car and my case is in the boot.
8. We go on breathing when we're asleep.
9. You're taller than me but I'm stronger than you.
10. Your watch is in the bathroom. It's on the basin.
11. If the car's in the garage, Dad's home.
12. There's the doorbell! The postman's early today.
13. That's Fred, but who's this?
14. You're not to telephone Granny now. It's too late.

C
- 3. It's not
- 6. That's not
- 9. Susan isn't
- 11. My book isn't
- 4. Robert's not
- 7. We aren't
- 10. The window's not
- 12. Aren't I
- 5. You aren't
- 8. He's not

D
- 2. There are
- 5. Is there
- 8. Are there
- 11. There's
- 14. there's
- 3. Are there
- 6. There's
- 9. are there
- 12. is there
- 4. There are
- 7. There isn't
- 10. There aren't
- 13. Is there

10 VERBS: SIMPLE PRESENT AND PRESENT CONTINUOUS

A
- 2. enjoy
- 4. finishes, goes
- 6. yawns, lies, stretches
- 8. fixes, sees
- 10. reaches, replies
- 12. buzzes, flies
- 3. stays, snows
- 5. march
- 7. cries, wakes
- 9. fizzes, stays
- 11. obey, try

B
- 2. I'm writing
- 4. We're swimming
- 6. The dog's chasing
- 8. David's puzzling
- 10. You're tickling
- 12. They're arguing
- 3. It's beginning
- 5. Sue and Pete are barbecuing
- 7. The weather's improving
- 9. The girls are dancing
- 11. Sally's signalling

C
- 3. cycles
- 5. knows
- 7. make
- 9. want
- 11. forgets
- 13. I'm trying
- 15. I think it's raining
- 4. breathe
- 6. are blowing
- 8. Susan's keying
- 10. are appearing
- 12. loves
- 14. Mum's doing

D
- 3. Who's making
- 5. are coming
- 7. begins
- 9. I'm meeting
- 11. What's happening
- 4. start or we're starting
- 6. Jim's getting
- 8. opens
- 10. are visiting
- 12. goes

11 SIMPLE PAST AND PAST CONTINUOUS

A
- 2. eyed
- 5. doubled
- 8. journeyed
- 11. paid
- 3. tried
- 6. pardoned
- 9. occupied
- 12. hurried
- 4. dialled
- 7. patted
- 10. tiptoed

B
- 2. weren't not, were
- 4. Were, weren't not
- 6. wasn't not, were
- 8. were, were
- 10. weren't not, was
- 12. wasn't not, wasn't not
- 3. was, wasn't not
- 5. was, weren't not
- 7. wasn't not, was
- 9. were, was
- 11. wasn't not, was

C
- 5. was thundering
- 7. wasn't not lying
- 9. Were you trying
- 11. weren't not singing
- 13. were carrying
- 15. Was anybody sitting
- 6. was writing
- 8. were listening
- 10. was tapping
- 12. was Harry saying
- 14. were queuing
- 16. was the bell ringing

D
- 3. was staring, noticed
- 5. were wandering, spotted
- 7. were you going, met
- 9. were watching, heard
- 11. called, was just finishing
- 4. was still sleeping, landed
- 6. were all running, walked
- 8. came, was still getting
- 10. was cutting, began
- 12. was thinking, struck

12 HAVE

A
- 3. has, have
- 7. having
- 11. having
- 15. have
- 4. had
- 8. had
- 12. had
- 16. having
- 5. having
- 9. has
- 13. has
- 6. have
- 10. have
- 14. has

B
- 3. I've already seen
- 5. Have you found
- 7. haven't not bought
- 9. Has somebody sat
- 11. Philip's won
- 13. have they parked
- 15. The sun's gone
- 4. You've spelt (or spelled)
- 6. There's been
- 8. What's happened
- 10. It's stopped
- 12. Who's already visited
- 14. hasn't not begun
- 16. haven't not thrown

C
3. Joe's got to finish his maths.
4. Have you got a computer of your own?
5. They have some new videos in the shop.
6. I haven't got enough money for the bus.
7. Who has my handphone?
8. Miss Lee's got an apartment near the school.
9. Has Jane got any brothers or sisters?
10. Bob's got only one sister.
11. Pigs have got curly tails.
12. We have to go now.

D
- 3. lost yesterday
- 5. They've already decided
- 7. The programme's just finished
- 8. crashed this morning
- 4. disappeared last night
- 6. landed five minutes ago
- 9. danced till dawn

2

10. The kettle's just boiled 11. escaped last night
12. rang on Christmas Day

13 DO

A
3. does, do   4. did   5. doing   6. do
7. did   8. do   9. does   10. did

B
3. don't, eat   4. doesn't like
5. didn't work   6. doesn't think
7. doesn't often play   8. doesn't snow
9. don't always travel   10. didn't catch
11. don't leave   12. didn't sleep
13. doesn't give   14. doesn't usually get

C
3. do you want
4. Did you visit
5. Do the twins like
6. What does a mynah bird sound
7. Do these trees produce
8. Does your mum enjoy
9. To whom did you address
10. Why did Miss Lee mark
11. Does the bus stop
12. Do you know
13. How did you do
14. Do all tarantulas have

D
3. Has the ball got to land in this square?
4. Do you have any brothers or sisters?
5. Has your mum got a map of the town?
6. Manx cats haven't got tails.
7. I don't have to leave yet.
8. Have we got to bring our own sandwiches?
9. What do you have in that box?
10. I haven't got the slightest idea what you mean.
11. Have they got enough food for all of us?
12. You haven't got to shout like that.

14 SHORT ANSWERS AND QUESTION TAGS

A
3. it is   4. he does   5. I don't
6. we were   7. they are   8. you are
9. I did   10. it has   11. he isn't
12. I haven't   13. I did   14. she wasn't

B
3. he is   4. she does   5. they are
6. they have   7. it is   8. it does
9. she does   10. it was   11. she did
12. he is   13. you did   14. they do

C
3. doesn't it?   4. don't they?   5. isn't it?
6. haven't you?   7. isn't there?   8. don't they?
9. didn't she?   10. didn't it?   11. haven't they?
12. isn't it?   13. aren't I?   14. don't we?

D
3. was it?   4. did he?   5. are they?
6. did you?   7. do we?   8. have you?
9. does it?   10. are we?   11. did they?
12. is it?   13. are there?   14. do you?

15 THE HELPING VERBS SHALL AND WILL: THE FUTURE

A
2. will   3. shall   4. won't not
5. will   6. will   7. won't not
8. Will   9. shall   10. will
11. shan't not   12. shall, won't not   13. won't not
14. will   15. Shall   16. won't not

B
3. won't   4. shall   5. won't   6. shall
7. won't   8. won't   9. won't   10. will
11. shan't   12. won't   13. will   14. won't

C
3. won't not be arriving
4. I'll (or I shall) be getting
5. will be opening
6. will be collecting
7. We'll (or we shall) be having
8. Will you be passing
9. I shan't (or won't) not be going
10. will be sailing
11. Shall (or will) I be seeing
12. will be closing
13. We'll (or we shall) be starting
14. won't not be playing

D
3. there is   4. you won't   5. I'm not
6. it will   7. they are   8. it won't
9. I won't (or I shan't)   10. there won't
11. you won't   12. she will   13. I am
14. you won't

16 THE HELPING VERBS CAN, COULD, WOULD

A1
3. Can you ski? No, I can't
4. can draw, can paint, can't sing
5. can't park
6. can't find
7. can hear
8. Can you touch? Yes, I can

A2
2. couldn't remember   3. could hear
4. couldn't sleep   5. could see
6. couldn't decide   7. could win
8. could hear, couldn't find

B
2. could you pass   3. Could/can I have
4. Could you give   5. Could/Can I read
6. could you turn off   7. Could you carry
8. Could/can I get   9. could/can I have
10. Could/Can I use   11. Could you tell
12. could you speak

C
2. she'd help   3. wouldn't start   4. he'd mend
5. wouldn't stop   6. I'd be   7. wouldn't obey
8. wouldn't open   9. they'd buy   10. you'd enjoy

D1
2. Where would you like to go today?
3. Would you like to rest now?
4. Would you like to watch it?
5. Would you like to come shopping with me this morning?
6. Would like a glass of juice?
7. Would you like ice cream for dessert?
8. Would you like some more noodles?

D2
2. I'd like to buy some stamps.
3. I'd like a drink of water.
4. I'd like to go swimming.
5. I'd love to come to your party.
6. I'd like to leave at 7.30.
7. I'd like a boiled egg and some toast.
8. I'd like to finish this bit of work.

17 THE HELPING VERBS MAY, MIGHT, MUST, SHOULD

A
3. You may bring; you may not use
4. May we go; you may not
5. May I access; you may
6. Danny may have; he may not stay
7. May Carol try; she may
8. May Tom put; he may
9. May I turn on; you may not
10. May Frankie and Harry play; they may

B
3. may see   4. may not find   5. might enjoy
6. may be   7. may get   8. may want
9. might slip   10. may help   11. may spend
12. may break

C
3. must finish   4. must have   5. mustn't alter
6. don't have to   7. must tell   8. had to wait
9. mustn't leave   10. had to open   11. must write
12. didn't have to wear

D
3. should read; You ought to read the exam paper carefully before beginning to write.
4. should make; Sally ought to make more use of her acting talents.
5. shouldn't try; You ought not to try to do so many things at once.
6. shouldn't eat; You ought not to eat so much fatty food.
7. shouldn't let; They ought not to let their dog's barking disturb the neighbours.
8. should think; You ought to think carefully before you decide.

18 MORE TENSES

A
2. hadn't seen   3. I'd taken
4. we'd done   5. I'd left
6. had disappeared   7. I'd lost
8. had brought   9. I'd found
10. had rescued   11. had happened
12. hadn't turned

3

B 3. won't ~~not~~ have woken
4. you'll have settled
5. they'll have arrived
6. I won't (or shan't) ~~not~~ have had
7. Will you already have started
8. will have recovered
9. it'll have opened
10. will have learnt

C 2. have been digging   3. You've been making
4. Have you been hurrying   5. We've been learning
6. have you been doing   7. Has Jane been crying
8. I've been trying   9. He's been exercising
10. who's (or who has) been using

D 2. had been snowing   3. had been working
4. I'd been wondering   5. had been training
6. she'd been gardening   7. hadn't been studying
8. had been running   9. I'd been eating
10. hadn't been waiting

19 TRANSITIVE AND INTRANSITVE

A 3. climb – transitive – the ladder, fit – transitive – a new light bulb
4. put – transitive – my pencil-sharpener
5. come – intransitive
6. go (out) – intransitive, buy – transitive – three bottles of juice and some bread
7. catch – transitive – the train
8. leave – transitive – school
9. have – transitive – another sandwich
10. die – intransitive, eat – intransitive, drink – intransitive
11. turn – intransitive, reach – transitive – the supermarket
12. talk – intransitive, wake – transitive – the baby.

B 2. tell (V), me (IO), the whole story (DO)
3. hand (V), me (IO), that list (DO)
4. send (V), Granny (IO), a postcard (DO)
5. sing (V), us (IO), his favourite song (DO)
6. give (V), everybody (IO), a piece of cake (DO)
7. build (V), his rabbit (IO), a hutch (DO)
8. lend (V), Peter (IO), his bicycle (DO)
9. play (V), her teacher (IO), the new piano piece. (DO)
10. read (V), me (IO), the second question (DO)
11. fetch (V), me (IO), another pack of paper (DO)
12. cook (V), her friends (IO), a delicious meal (DO)

C 2a. stand (I)   2b. stand (T)   3a. opened (I)
3b. open (T)   4a. draws (I)   4b. drawn (T)
5a. played (T)   5b. playing (I)   6a. watched (T)
6b. Watch (I)   7a. lost (I)   7b. losing (T)
8a. changes (T)   8b. change (I)

D 2. (I) Move back to let the ambulance pass. (T) Move your eyes from side to side.
3. (I) Ride with both hands on the handlebars. (T) Ride your bicycle carefully in the traffic.
4. (I) Dress neatly for school. (T) Dress the baby for me.
5. (I) Walk twice round the block. (T) Walk your dog every day.
6. (I) Clap in time to the music. (T) Clap this rhythm.
7. (I) Swing on this rope. (T) Swing your arms as you walk.
8. (I) Study hard if you want to do well. (T) Study this diagram carefully.

20 THE PASSIVE

A 2. St Paul's Cathedral was designed by Sir Christopher Wren.
3. The part of the wicked uncle was played by Vincent.
4. This poem was written by Wordsworth.
5. The school is opened at 8.00 by the caretaker.
6. The football team is trained by Mr Kwo.
7. I was stung on the arm by a bee.
8. Singapore was founded by Sir Stamford Raffles.
9. These books were collected by my grandfather.
10. This apartment block is owned by the government.
11. In 1941 the house was destroyed by a bomb.
12. I was knocked off my bike by a taxi.

B 3. Mum's present was wrapped in coloured paper.
4. The street was crowded with people.
5. The seeds were carried by the wind.
6. The prince was clothed in fine robes.
7. Maggie's wardrobe was crammed with clothes.
8. The ship was hit by a torpedo.
9. The air was filled with strange noises.
10. The damage was caused by a hurricane.
11. Sue was dressed in purple.
12. The drawer was crammed with papers.

C 2. A lot of litter had been dropped by the picnickers.
3. The car has been repaired by the mechanic.
4. Our van was being towed away by the police.
5. My brother is being taught to drive by my dad.
6. Those bumps in the lawn have been made by a mole.
7. The part of the First Ugly Sister will be read by Mary.
8. Our lives have been completely changed by computers.
9. The scenery for the play is being made by the pupils.
10. Some rubbish had been left in the drive by the builders.
11. The prizes are being presented by the head teacher's daughter.
12. Refreshments will be provided by a catering firm.

D1 2. The passengers were told that the train was running late.
3. We were asked to wait in a queue.
4. Has the lamp post been mended?
5. These papers were left on the table.
6. The prisoners were ordered to go back to their cells.
7. Have the bedrooms been cleaned?
8. Dinner is served between six o'clock and nine o'clock.

D2 2. It is said that eating a lot of eggs is bad for you.
3. It is not (or it isn't) known who invented the wheel.
4. It is believed that holidays help you to relax.
5. It is thought that the illness comes from eating rotten fruit.
6. It is known that the stars are getting further apart.
7. It is said that a good education is the key to success.
8. It is believed that the man was murdered.

21 MORE PRACTICE WITH QUESTION TAGS

A 3. will you?   4. don't they?   5. couldn't he?
6. isn't there?   7. didn't she?   8. isn't it?
9. had he?   10. weren't you?   11. must we?
12. aren't they?

B 2. couldn't you?   3. mustn't she?   4. couldn't we?
5. wouldn't it?   6. couldn't she?   7. wouldn't he?
8. mustn't there?   9. couldn't they?   10. would they?

C 2. wouldn't they?   3. mustn't it?
4. couldn't you?   5. wouldn't they?
6. shouldn't I?   7. won't we? (or shan't we?)
8. would it?   9. mustn't it?
10. couldn't she?

D 3. wasn't he?   4. hasn't he?   5. isn't it?
6. was it?   7. won't it?   8. hadn't they?
9. haven't you?   10. hadn't it?

22 -ING NOUNS AND TO-INFINITIVES

A 2. baking   3. going   4. climbing
5. working   6. tidying   7. brushing
8. raining   9. doing   10. arriving
11. getting   12. crying

B 2. to leave   3. to take   4. to travel
5. to hurt   6. to train   7. to meet
8. to sing   9. to hold, to rain   10. to walk
11. to listen   12. to write

C 2. to take   3. to fix
4. practising (or to practise)   5. to carry
6. eating   7. to miss
8. to write (or writing)   9. to drive
10. sleeping   11. walking
12. spending   13. to return
14. listening (or to listen)

D 2. uncomfortable to sit   3. nothing to do
4. difficult to see   5. nice to eat
6. afraid to ask   7. space to park
8. unlikely to pass   9. tasks to complete
10. anything to read   11. exciting to watch
12. something to drink

23 ADVERBS (1)

A 2. neatly   3. loudly, quietly
4. carefully   5. comfortably
6. angrily   7. musically
8. easily   9. suddenly
10. gradually, brightly   11. briskly
12. clearly

B 2. adverb   3. adverb   4. adjective   5. adjective
6. adverb   7. adjective   8. adverb   9. adjective
10. adjective   11. adjective   12. adjective   13. adverb
14. adjective

C
2. hardly   3. lately   4. hard, well   5. most
6. nearly   7. late   8. last   9. well
10. fine   11. mostly   12. justly

D
2. outside   3. slowly along the street
4. When   5. absolutely
6. Never   7. yet
8. for three weeks.   9. into the bin
10. just   11. rudely, severely
12. How, fast

24 ADVERBS (2)

A
2. far   3. a lot   4. long
5. much   6. long, a lot   7. a long way
8. far   9. a long time

B
3. quite badly   4. fairly badly   5. very badly
6. very well   7. rather badly   8. fairly well
9. extremely well   10. rather well

C
2. Fortunately the bus hadn't left.
3. Fortunately I had some bandages in my pack.
4. Unfortunately we found that it was blocked by an accident.
5. Fortunately I'd remembered to buy him a card.
6. Fortunately Miss Lee didn't notice it.
7. Unfortunately I dropped them on the way home.
8. Unfortunately it started to rain heavily.
9. Unfortunately I've hurt my ankle.
10. Fortunately she wasn't hurt.

D
2. Susan has always worked hard at school.
3. The twins both want to become doctors.
4. Mary had already laid the table.
5. The plane has just landed.
6. They each received a copy of the rules.
7. My parents sometimes travel abroad.
8. Dad rarely comes home before eight o'clock.
9. I've often thought about you.
10. Dave also knew the answer.
11. We were all pleased with our results.
12. Do you usually watch television after dinner?
13. Are you still working at the café?
14. He never replies to my e-mails.
15. People don't always tell you the complete truth.
16. What do you usually have for breakfast?

25 COMPARISON

A
2. more quickly   3. most successfully
4. more economically   5. most humbly
6. most clumsily   7. more simply
8. more easily   9. more accurately
10. most speedily

B
2. earlier   3. farther (or further)
4. most imaginatively   5. harder
6. later   7. more tidily
8. better   9. longest
10. sooner   11. more
12. worst

C
2. much better   3. a bit younger
4. a bit farther (or further)   5. a bit smaller
6. much larger   7. much nearer
8. much earlier   9. a bit longer
10. much later

D
3. Our apartment isn't as big as the Lees' apartment.
4. Sally isn't as untidy as Mary.
5. Kenneth doesn't live as near to the school as me (or as I do).
6. Mum doesn't enjoy television as much as Dad.
7. Judy isn't as shy as she used to be.
8. My sister doesn't weigh as much as me (or as I do).
9. English isn't as difficult as maths.
10. I'm not as keen on dancing as Helen.

26 PREPOSITIONS (1)

A
2. up   3. of   4. after
5. before   6. of, over   7. on, across
8. with, on   9. into, to   10. on, into
11. to, at   12. without   13. during
14. to, at   15. of, opposite

B
2. through (the door)   3. into (me)
4. in (Tokyo)   5. to (Julia)
6. of (Cinderella)   7. by (Shakespeare)

8. against (Peter)   9. in (it)
10. than (Joe), than (me)   11. over (the wall)
12. with (his brother)
13. from (the corner), for (Miss Lee)
14. at (this strange insect), on (my hand)

C
2. on top of the bookcase   3. out of your desks
4. next to me   5. away from the electric fence
6. on board the ship   7. on to the platform
8. in between my toes   9. in front of the hotel
10. as far as the corner   11. up to us
12. all over his shirt   13. ahead of the others
14. along with you

D
2. preposition   3. adverb   4. adverb
5. preposition   6. adverb   7. preposition
8. preposition   9. preposition   10. adverb
11. preposition   12. adverb   13. adverb
14. preposition

27 PREPOSITIONS (2)

A
2. in   3. on to   4. on   5. into
6. on   7. into   8. on   9. into
10. on   11. on to   12. in

B
2. by   3. in   4. to   5. by, on
6. to, by   7. in, from   8. on   9. by
10. on   11. by   12. on

C
2. On, after   3. for
4. from, to (or till or until)   5. at
6. before   7. After, for
8. at, at   9. In, at, past
10. from, to, to (or till or until), past
11. After, till (or until), past   12. during (or in)

D
2. in, against   3. except   4. of   5. at, of
6. without   7. on   8. by   9. instead of
10. with   11. at, of   12. on   13. with
14. on   15. like

28 PREPOSITIONS (3)

A
2. for   3. at   4. of   5. for
6. with   7. of   8. for   9. to
10. to   11. in   12. to   13. with
14. for   15. from   16. in

B
2. on fishing   3. in dancing   4. of thanking
5. on driving   6. of sitting   7. of calculating
8. on winning   9. of reading   10. at getting

C
2. sitting on   3. row the boat with
4. talk to   5. look at
6. resting your feet on   7. rely on
8. park the car in   9. putting the rubbish into
10. hanging your coats on

D1
2. The possibility is being looked into.
3. The problem was argued about for hours.
4. The figures have been checked through.

D2
2. What is Dad angry about?
3. What is Bob listening to?
4. Who did Mary dance with?

D3
2. The man that Dad is speaking to is the manager.
3. The apartment that we are going to look at is in Bread Street.
4. The old friend that I bumped into today was on holiday here.

29 PHRASAL VERBS (1)

A
2. broken down = to be not working
3. grow up = to become an adult
4. join in = to take part
5. take off = to leave the runway
6. Watch out = to notice danger and take care
7. shut up = to stop talking
8. get along = to be friendly with somebody
9. show off = to do things to make people notice you
10. give up = to stop trying

B
2. call off (the match) = to cancel
3. mixing (the twins) up = to confuse
4. put out (the fire) = to extinguish
5. make up (a story) = to invent

5

6. blow up (the tower) = to explode
7. turn (the television) off = to stop an electrical thing working
8. Take off (your coat) = to remove
9. brought up (three children) = to rear
10. burnt (the shop) down = to destroy by fire

C 2. agree with (Dad) = to have the same opinion
3. looking for (my schoolbag) = to try to find
4. changed into (a beetle) = to be transformed
5. laughed at (Joe's joke) = to be amused by something
6. Aim carefully at (the target) = to point a weapon at something
7. get off (the bus) = to leave a vehicle
8. belong to (me) = to be possessed by somebody
9. look after (patients) = to take care of somebody
10. jump at (the chance) = to accept an opportunity eagerly

D 2. gone off with (my calculator)
3. going in for (competitions)
4. keep up with (you)
5. running away from (your problems)
6. run out of (food)
7. look down on (the younger ones)
8. put up with (the cold)
9. stands up for (me)
10. come out in (red spots)

30 PHRASAL VERBS (2)

A 3. up — adverb   4. through — preposition
5. round — adverb   6. up — adverb
7. down — adverb   8. into — preposition
9. down — adverb, to — preposition
10. together — adverb

B 2. The curtains go with the carpet but the cushions don't go with it.
3. The soldiers laid explosives under the bridge and blew it up.
4. I want to finish off my essay (or finish my essay off) before I go to bed.
5. You can always depend on her to help.
6. They made some bad mistakes and tried to cover them up.
7. They are threatening to close down the school (or close the school down) next year.
8. Miss Lee handed out the exam papers (or handed the exam papers out) at nine-thirty.
9. Pick up all these toys (or pick all these toys up) and put them away.
10. Hang up your coat (or hang your coat up) before somebody trips over it.

C 2. A notice was sent round by the head teacher.
3. Their addresses were mixed up by the post office.
4. Harry was sometimes laughed at by the other children.
5. The electricity had already been turned off by Dad.
6. My name has been crossed out by somebody.
7. He was beaten up by a gang of bullies last night.
8. These dishes were left behind by Jill.
9. The baby is being cared for by some friends.
10. I was soon caught up by the rest of the group.

D1 2. Here are some dry clothes that you can change into.
3. Have you a question that you would like to bring up?
4. There's still a problem that we must deal with.
5. We all need goals that we can aim for.

D2 7. Here's a raincoat to put on.
8. These are the right choices to go for.
9. I'm giving you an application form to fill in.
10. I have some more ideas to come back to later.

31 CO-ORDINATING CONJUNCTIONS: AND, BUT, OR, SO

A 2. and   3. and   4. or   5. or
6. but   7. or   8. but   9. and
10. or   11. but   12. or

B 2. We don't need any carrots, potatoes, onions, cooking oil or noodles.
3. This morning I have maths, English, music, history and computer studies.
4. Shall we watch television, go for a walk or play football?
5. Find a large sheet of paper, some coloured pens and a pair of scissors.

6. I must finish my homework, call Mary, mend my bicycle and write to Granny.
7. I don't know whether to go swimming, sort out my photographs or tidy my bedroom.
8. Pollution is a danger to wildlife, rivers and lakes, plants and the atmosphere.
9. Is a spider an insect, an animal or what?

C 2. Would you like to come to my house or shall I come to yours?
3. Jim is performing some acrobatics and the others are watching him.
4. I called Granny but she wasn't at home.
5. Take these sausages and put them in the fridge.
6. I want to copy this material into another file but I don't know how to do it.
7. You may unfasten your seatbelts now but you may not smoke on this aircraft.
8. Find a partner and hold hands.
9. Will Peter win or will Robert beat him?
10. It was raining hard so we decided to cancel the barbecue.

D 2. Hurry up or you'll miss your bus.
3. Stop pulling my hair or I'll tell Mum.
4. Do some work or you'll fail your exams.
5. Hold on to the rail or you'll slip.
6. Move your bicycle or somebody will trip over it.
7. Have your soup now or it'll get cold.
8. Tell me the truth or you'll get no pocket money.
9. Lend me your handphone or I won't help you.
10. Act now or you'll miss your chance.

32 CONJUNCTIONS AND CLAUSES (1)

A 2. Give Jane this message _when_ you see her.
3. We felt very sad _as_ we said goodbye.
4. _After_ I've eaten my breakfast, I'm ready to face the day.
5. I cooked a meal for the guests _while_ they washed and changed.
6. _As soon as_ Peter got home, he fed his pet rabbit.
7. _When_ the sun rose, the birds began to sing.
8. _While_ the car park is being altered, we'll have to park in the street.
9. _When_ you were in India, did you see the Taj Mahal?
10. Wait quietly at the bus stop _till_ the bus comes.

B 3. goes   4. comes   5. leave
6. I'll contact   7. arrives   8. makes
9. start   10. I'll tell

C 2. remembers   3. applies   4. She'll get
5. come   6. does   7. there's
8. works   9. buy   10. rains

D 3. hadn't ~~not~~ sneezed   4. got
5. had   6. found
7. were   8. hadn't ~~not~~ forgotten
9. had come   10. didn't ~~not~~ care

33 CONJUNCTIONS AND CLAUSES (2)

A 2. I had a headache
3. you're the eldest
4. he isn't old enough
5. Take a book to read
6. you weren't at the café
7. We'll take the tram
8. you may hurt somebody's feelings
9. it's the last day of term,
10. You tell me the answer then,

B 2. so that (or in order that)   3. so that (or in order that)
4. so as to (or in order to)   5. so that (or in order that)
6. so that (or in order that)   7. so as to (or in order to)
8. so as to (or in order to)   9. so that (or in order that)
10. so as to (or in order to)

C 2. so   3. so   4. such a   5. such a
6. so   7. such a   8. such   9. so
10. such

D 1. the grammar is difficult
2. I had to sing a solo at the concert
3. you aren't successful
4. he's still in good health
5. you think it sounds silly
6. We started the second book
7. Everybody's welcome to join the course
8. she's only ten herself
9. she's good at drawing horses
10. Mum usually laughs

6

34 **RELATIVE CLAUSES:** *WHO, WHOM, WHICH, THAT*

A
2. who performs operations.
3. who fits showers and mends pipes.
4. which helps you do sums.
5. which supports your head.
6. which has prickles to protect it.
7. who plays the flute.
8. which measures temperature.
9. which is man-made.
10. who watch an event.

B
3. The doctor who (or that) treated my injury was from Thailand.
4. The umbrella Anna lent me is hanging over there.
5. The strange noise that (or which) woke us in the night was the foghorn.
6. The friend I was trying to contact was away on holiday.
7. The passengers we made friends with were Scottish.
8. The hair-dryer Jane bought was faulty.
9. The armchair you're sitting in was my mother's.
10. The man who (or that) opened the door was tall and thin.

C1
2. The shop where I bought your present is closing down.
3. The youth hostel where they stayed was very comfortable.
4. The hall where we're performing our concert holds 1000 people.
5. The shelf where the dictionary sits is over there.

C2
2. The bench I was sitting on was not very steady.
3. The park the children play in has swings and a climbing frame.
4. The hotel they stayed at had a swimming pool.
5. The book I found the map in is kept in the car.

D
3. The door was opened by Harry, who was wearing his gym clothes.
4. We went to look for our car, which we had parked in a side street.
5. Jennifer is going to marry Steven, whom (or who) she met at a dance.
6. We visited the Tower of London, which stands beside the River Thames.
7. I waited in the Café Politique, where I'd arranged to meet Sue.
8. I've just been to the dentist, who said my teeth were in perfect condition.
9. We all met outside the hotel, where the bus was standing ready for us.
10. I had a long conversation with Angela, whom (or who) I hadn't seen for three years.

35 **NOUN CLAUSES**

A
2. that she wants to be a musician
3. that I left my calculator in my desk
4. that he's moving house soon
5. that I shouldn't eat so much
6. that the match was cancelled
7. that Mum could use the computer
8. that the earthquake was only a small one
9. that she was the right person for the job
10. that the flight was on time

B
2. the apartment would be available in two weeks' time
3. he can't win
4. the plan will succeed
5. you were looking for me
6. you painted that picture yourself
7. he just died in his sleep
8. it's right to kill insects
9. you don't want to listen to all that nonsense
10. you were going out tonight

C
2. if (or whether) the washing machine had finished
3. if (or whether) she's better yet
4. if (or whether) we'd brought our atlases to school
5. if (or whether) it's going to clear up
6. if (or whether) the others are awake yet
7. if (or whether) he can drive you to your dancing class
8. if (or whether) the train from Leeds had arrived
9. if (or whether) she's any good at acting
10. if (or whether) he'll remember to bring his kit

D
2. when   3. who (or whom)   4. what
5. how   6. why   7. which
8. who   9. where   10. what

36 **PHRASES**

A
2. I'm giving you _some grammar exercises_ for _your English homework_.
3. We're performing *Macbeth*, _one of Shakespeare's plays_.
4. I found _some pretty shells_ on _the beach_ and added them to _my large collection_.

5. Mary, _my cousin from London_, is visiting us soon.
6. Lucy examined _the curious purple envelope_ carefully before opening it.
7. Look at _these splendid red apples_ that I bought at _the local supermarket_.
8. Joe gave _his last coin_ to _a ragged child_.
9. Yesterday I met Mark, _an old friend of mine_.
10. There are _three good reasons_ why I can't play in _Saturday's match_.

B
2. _For once_ the train arrived _on time_.
3. We shall be leaving _at four o'clock_.
4. Dad explained the process _in great detail_.
5. Come and sit _beside me_.
6. Watch _once again_, _a bit more carefully_.
7. We played tennis _until half past six_.
8. He walks _very slowly_ _with a stick_.
9. We're going abroad _during the vacation_.
10. _At least_ I played my part _pretty well_ _in the play_.

C
2. Ask the lady _in the blue uniform_.
3. The label _attached to the chicken_ gives cooking instructions.
4. Who sits at the desk _in the corner_?
5. Dad was talking to a man _with a beard_.
6. They collect money for people _without homes_.
7. The path _through the park_ was muddy.
8. The pictures _on the wall_ were all drawn by the children.
9. The man _standing in front of me_ suddenly stepped backwards.
10. Is this the bus _for Melaka_?

D
2. She's a two-month-old baby.
3. We're a two-car family.
4. We had a two-hour delay.
5. It's an eight-page booklet.
6. They use up-to-date methods.
7. It's horrible-smelling cheese.
8. It is an eighteenth-century house.
9. It's a very odd-looking building.
10. It was a three-day journey.

37 **NEGATIVE SENTENCES**

A
3. We may not have finished the job by next week.
4. I wouldn't like to live in Africa.
5. I cannot imagine what she was thinking.
6. Learning French at school might not have changed my life.
7. This is the kind of silly behaviour teachers should not ignore.
8. You can't park your car over there.
9. She said she wouldn't be here tomorrow.
10. She won't come back again.

B
3. He doesn't eat a lot of fish.
4. I don't understand the question.
5. The man did not hesitate for a second before jumping out of the plane.
6. We didn't see Mary in town this morning.
7. Who doesn't want coffee?
8. The children did not sleep all night.
9. They didn't manage to pull the sheep out of the ditch.
10. I didn't know what to do.
11. The policeman didn't ask for our names.
12. The boys did not think they had enough money for the train fare home.

C
2. We have no food left.
3. There is nobody in the garden.
4. There is nothing wrong with the car.
5. There is no-one else I can ask for help.
6. 'How many sums did you get wrong?' 'None.'
7. None of the passengers in the train were (or was) injured in the crash.
8. No passengers were injured in the crash.
9. There were two men in the shop. Neither of them spoke English.
10. There were three men in the shop. None of them spoke English.

D
3. We might not buy any more bread.
4. My sister says she never meets anyone interesting at her friend's parties.
5. She may not have anything important to tell you.
6. There won't be anyone to help you carry your bags.
7. There might not be anything anyone could do to help them.
8. My sister hasn't been invited to the party and I haven't been invited either.
9. She doesn't drink tea and she doesn't drink coffee either.
10. No voting stations are open yet.
11. I haven't had lunch yet.
12. None of your friends have brought any food with them either.

QUESTIONS

A 2. Will they have finished the project by the end of next week?
3. Must we leave at once?
4. Is he coming round to see us tomorrow night?
5. Was she very upset when she heard the news?
6. Do the boys want to come with us to the circus?
7. Was she a close friend of the head teacher?
8. Did she say she was a close friend of the head teacher?
9. Is there something wrong with my calculations?
10. Were the children singing as they walked through the woods?

B 3. Wouldn't they be able to help you?
4. Isn't it time the children were in bed?
5. Didn't we see that man on television last night?
6. Couldn't you have invited them to the wedding?
7. Can the boys not stay a little bit longer?
8. Have they never been to France?
9. Do her parents not like pop music?
10. Doesn't the hedge need cutting again?

C 2. How did you get here?
3. What happened?
4. When did you get here?
5. Whose books are these?
6. Who (or whom) should I send the letter to?
7. To whom should I send the letter?
8. Which cake would you like?
9. Why do I have to go to bed now?
10. To what do you owe your success?

D 2. Oh? what's it like?
3. What (or How) about giving her some flowers or a pot plant?
4. How do you do?
5. What time is it?
6. What is it like being the youngest dancer in the company?
7. How (or What) about you?
8. What's the matter?
9. What if no-one heard you calling for help?
10. Oh? What are they like?

39 **REPORTED SPEECH**

A 2. were 3. hadn't 4. was 5. weren't
6. Sheila's 7. had 8. didn't 9. left
10. we'd

B 3. I'd 4. she'd 5. couldn't
6. would 7. was, wouldn't 8. hated
9. couldn't 10. had

C 2. Sarah told her brother that she was sick and tired of his laziness.
3. I said that I was surprised to see her there.
4. The girl said that she didn't like coffee.
5. Mary told her friend that her sister was going to be a nurse.
6. The children told the police that they had seen a strange man outside the shop just before the robbery.
7. The couple next door told me that they had taught English in Japan for a year.
8. She complained that her leg hurt.
9. Arnie said he would be back.
10. Tom said that he couldn't come the next day (or the following day).

D 2. I asked her what she was thinking.
3. The doctor asked him how he had been feeling the day before (or the previous day).
4. The vet asked if (or whether) the horse had been fed that morning.
5. She asked the painter if (or whether) he would be finished by the next day (or the following day).
6. I wondered if (or whether) everyone had gone home.
7. They asked the little girl if (or whether) she wanted to watch television with them.
8. Tom asked how to switch on the computer.
9. Mary asked Fred where to put his books.
10. She asked him what his children called his father's new wife.

E 3. The colonel commanded his company to halt.
4. The doctor advised Dad to take a week's holiday.
5. The notice forbids us to enter.
6. Mum asked me to help her with the beds.
7. The guide warned the tourists to take care on the steps.
8. We persuaded Granny to stay till the next day (or the following day).
9. Miss Lee told us not to look at the answers.
10. The sign requested us to wipe our feet.

40 **PUNCTUATION**

A 1. Tom had an extra helping of ice-cream.
2. Is there anything I can do to help?
3. What are you going to do with that?
4. What you did was a complete waste of time.
5. There's enough for everyone, isn't there?
6. Help! I'm drowning!
7. She asked him what he was intending to do.
8. Good morning! (or Good morning.) How are you today?
9. You idiot! You've broken my favourite vase.
10. What I want to know is whether or not you're willing to help us.
11. Do you think you could move over a bit?
12. Stop that at once!

B 1. Could I have another glass of water, please?
2. Excuse me, madam. Is that your purse on the floor?
3. Please, John, don't do that.
4. Oh, I'm so glad you managed to come, my dear.
5. Come along, children. Yes, you too, James.
6. No, no, no, not these ones! I want those pink ones over there.
7. I'm feeling very well, thank you.
8. Yes, that's the right answer. Well done, lad.
9. Well, here you are at last! You know, Liz, you really ought to try to be more punctual.
10. Believe me, it's no fun sleeping in a bus shelter in a thunderstorm.

C 1. He was followed into the room by a dirty, long-haired, nasty-looking dog.
2. This is a sure cure for coughs, colds, chills, fevers(,) and all sorts of aches and pains.
3. On the shelf were an odd assortment of boxes, bottles and tins.
4. The official languages of Singapore are English, Malay, Mandarin and Tamil.
5. With eating, drinking, talking, singing and dancing the evening passed all too quickly.
6. He was wearing a brown and grey jacket, grey trousers(,) and green boots.
7. I heard a loud, eerie, almost despairing cry.
8. She spoke rapidly, excitedly, with eyes flashing.
9. Let's eat, drink and be merry.
10. Peter, John and I are going to the football match tomorrow.

D 1. I'll be back in a moment. Don't go away. We've some things to discuss about next week's concert.
2. She doesn't know what she's supposed to do.
3. They've spent a lot of money on their children's Christmas presents.
4. It's a lovely little dog, isn't it?
5. I'm so glad you've come.
6. It's no wonder that the dog's scratching its ears. It's got fleas.
7. Let's go inside. I'll put on the kettle and we'll have a nice cup of tea.
8. The teachers searched through every student's locker.
9. The teachers searched through both boys' lockers.
10. Could you tell me where the men's department is, please?
11. I suppose that's some people's idea of fun, but it certainly isn't mine.
12. There's at least three weeks' more work to do here.

Determiners

Gerunds

Transitive
Verbs

Infinitive

Phrases

ound
ences

Comp
Sente

Question
Tags

Uncount
Nouns

Adject
Phra

Reflexive
Pronouns

Claus

LEARNERS
PUBLISHING

ISBN 981- 4070- 44- 0

9 789814 070447